DAD & me

JOURNALS® of a LIFETIME

made with love *from you to me*

www.JournalsOfALifetime.com

DAD & Me will take you on an interactive and fun journey, having a great time getting to know each other better.

Tips to enjoy DAD & Me :

- ⦿ Your questions are in orange. Dad's questions are in blue.

- ⦿ Dip in and complete your questions in any order, whenever you want.

- ⦿ Use words, drawings, doodles . . . whatever feels right for you.

- ⦿ There are no right or wrong answers, just your own.

- ⦿ Use the extra pages to capture anything else you would like to explore.

- ⦿ Agree when and how to share your pages with the other person.

- ⦿ Enjoy yourself and have fun!

A bit about Dad . . .

My full name :

My age :   Today's date :

A picture of Dad . . . a drawing or photo

DAD

A bit about Me . . .

My full name : Samuel James Luloff

My age : 8½   Today's date : 9/28/18

A picture of Me . . . a drawing or photo

Me

A bit about Dad . . .

What I love watching on television :

Best movies :

Top songs :

Favorite places :

Things I say a lot :

I love to eat :

DAD

A bit about Me . . .

What I love watching on television :

Best movies :

Top Songs :

Favorite places :

Things I say a lot :

I love to eat :

Me

Today . . .

Who I talked to :

What I did :

The best things :

The worst things :

What I wanted to do, but didn't get around to :

DAD

Today . . .

Who I talked to :

What I did :

The best things :

The worst things :

What I wanted to do, but didn't get around to :

Me

When I was younger . . .

My earliest memory :

What I was like :

When I was younger I thought that :

DAD

When I was younger . . .

My earliest memory :

What I was like :

When I was younger I thought that :

Me

Happened to me . . .

Funny things :

Embarrassing things :

Sad things :

DAD

Happened to me . . .

Funny things :

Embarrassing things :

Sad things :

Me

The way we are . . .

The ways we are Similar :

The ways we are different :

Things I admire about you :

DAD

The way we are . . .

The ways we are similar :

The ways we are different :

Things I admire about you :

Me

My family . . .

Some great memories of our family :

What I love about our family :

What I would like to be different :

DAD

My family . . .

Some great memories of our family :

What I love about our family :

What I would like to be different :

Me

Family times . . .

Things I love doing with my family :

I wish we could :

I wish we didn't :

DAD

Family times . . .

Things I love doing with my family :

I wish we could :

I wish we didn't :

Me

Where I live . . .

What I remember about the places I have lived :

Things at home that are special :

Where I might like to live in the future :

DAD

Where I live . . .

What I remember about the places I have lived :

Things at home that are special :

Where I might like to live in the future :

Me

Birthdays . . .

My best memories :

How I would like to spend future birthdays :

My perfect present would be :

DAD

Vacations . . .

My best memories :

The best places I have been :

Where I would love to visit :

Me

with friends . . .

How I feel about my friends :

What I admire most about you and your friends :

What I want to change about my friendships :

DAD

with friends . . .

How I feel about my friends :

What I admire most about you and your friends :

What I want to change about my friendships :

Me

Messages for my friends . . .

To

To

To

To

To

To

DAD

Messages for my friends . . .

To

To

To

To

To

To

Me

My spare time . . .

What I enjoy doing most in my spare time :

What I would love to do :

What I love watching you do :

DAD

My Spare time . . .

What I enjoy doing most in my spare time :

What I would love to do :

What I love you watching me do :

Me

School . . .

What I loved about being at school :

What I found most difficult :

With the benefit of hindsight :

DAD

School . . .

What I love about being at school :

What I find most difficult :

My greatest learning experience :

Me

Learning . . .

What I would love to learn :

How I best like to learn :

The help I would like from you :

DAD

Learning . . .

What I would love to learn :

How I best like to learn :

The help I would like from you :

Me

Books & stories . . .

Some of my favorite books :

Books I love that I hope you will read :

Books I would love to read :

DAD

Books & stories . . .

Some of my favorite books :

Favorite characters from my books :

Books I would love to read :

Me

Some of my favorite things . . .

DAD

Some of my favorite things . . .

Me

Growing up . . .

What was exciting :

What I was concerned about :

The help and guidance I received :

DAD

Growing up . . .

What is exciting :

What I am concerned about :

The help I would like :

Me

My body . . .

How I feel about me :

What I like about me :

What I would like to share with you :

DAD

My body . . .

How I feel about me :

What I like about me :

What I would like to share with you :

Me

Being healthy . . .

A drawing of my ideas to be fit and healthy :

DAD

Being healthy . . .

A drawing of my ideas to be fit and healthy :

Me

Feeling happy . . .

The things that make me happy :

What makes me feel confident :

Who I love spending time with :

DAD

Feeling happy . . .

The things that make me happy :

What makes me feel confident :

Who I love spending time with :

Me

Feeling sad . . .

The things that make me sad :

What shakes my confidence :

What helps me when I feel sad :

DAD

Feeling sad . . .

The things that make me sad :

What shakes my confidence :

What helps me when I feel sad :

Me

My worries . . .

Things that worry me :

Some of my regrets :

How I best manage any worries :

DAD

My worries . . .

Things that worry me :

Some of my regrets :

How I best manage any worries :

Me

Falling in love . . .

My views on love :

what is important to me :

My first love and what I learned :

DAD

Falling in love . . .

My views on love :

What is important to me :

What I have learnt so far :

Me

My future . . .

Things I want to do in my life :

Things I want to do with you :

Some words to describe the person I want to be :

DAD

My future . . .

Things I want to do in my life :

Things I want to do with you :

Some words to describe the person I want to be :

Me

My dreams . . .

What I dream about :

How I see my future :

What I wish I could spend more time doing :

DAD

My dreams . . .

What I dream about :

How I see my future :

What I wish I could spend more time doing :

Me

Dad & Me . . .

What I love about you :

What I love about us :

What I wish we could do more of :

DAD

Dad & Me . . . .

What I love about you :

What I love about us :

What I wish we could do more of :

Me

Thoughts I have . . .

In 5 years :

I hope :

Something you don't know about me :

DAD

Thoughts I have . . .

In 5 years :

I hope :

Something you don't know about me :

Me

Helping others . . .

People I admire who help others :

How I like to help others :

What I could do more :

DAD

Helping others . . .

People I admire who help others :

How I like to help others :

What I could do more :

Me

Topics of Dad's choice . . . .

These pages are for you, Dad, to write questions . . .

Topics of Dad's choice . . .

. . . or topics for you and your child to answer

Me

Topics of my choice . . .

These pages are for you to write questions . . .

DAD

Topics of my choice . . .

. . . or topics for you and your Dad to answer

Me

A poem about me & you . . .

DAD

A poem about me & you . . .

Me

A letter to myself based on what I have discovered in this journal . . .

Dear Me

DAD

A letter to myself based on what I
have discovered in this journal . . .

Dear Me

Me

Thinking about what I have discovered
from this journal, here is a picture
Showing my dreams for the future . . .

DAD

Thinking about what I have discovered from this journal, here is a picture showing my dreams for the future . . .

Me

Final thoughts & doodles . . .

Final thoughts & doodles . . .

Me

DAD & me

First published in the USA by *from you to me* February 2015. Reprinted January 2018.
Copyright from you to me limited 2015

ISBN 978-1-907048-67–8

Printed and bound in China by Imago.
This paper is manufactured from pulp sourced from forests that are legally and sustainably managed.

For more information please contact:

from you to me
The Old Brewery
Newtown
Bradford on Avon
BA15 1NF, UK

hello@fromyoutome.com
www.JournalsOfALifetime.com

Published by from you to me ltd

Share the things that really matter ... share your stories with our website community at www.JournalsOfALifetime.com where journals can also be personalised.